Usborne
Wipe-Clean
Animal
Activities

Illustrated by Manuela Berti

Designed by Laura Hammonds

Written by Kirsteen Robson

Use your wipe-clean pen to do all the
activities in this fun-filled book.

In the rainforest

Write an X under the monkey that does not match any other.

Draw more teeth in this crocodile's mouth.

Draw over the
dotted lines above
to finish the toucans.

Follow the trails
to see which
hummingbird
finds the flower.

Grassland animals

Use the pen to show the zebra the way to the watering hole.

Draw over the dotted lines to finish the African elephants.

Draw patches on the giraffe.

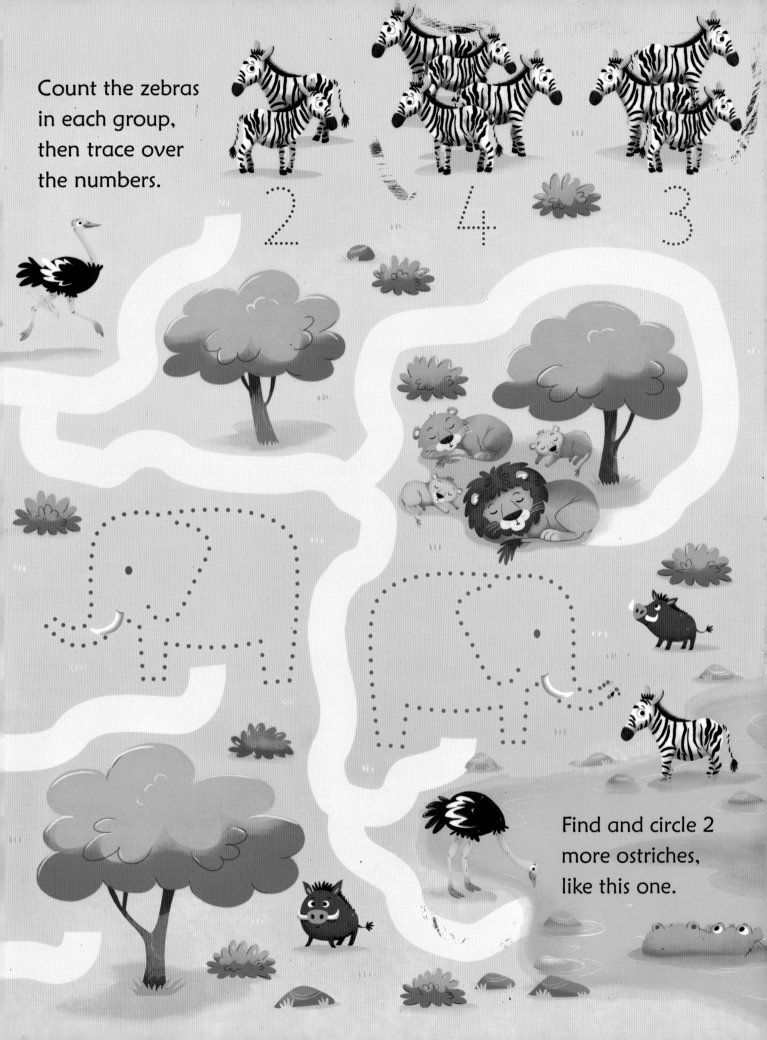

Count the zebras in each group, then trace over the numbers.

2   4   3

Find and circle 2 more ostriches, like this one.

Under the sea

Draw lines between the rays below that match each other.

Draw over the dotted lines to finish the turtles.

4 6 7

5 8

2 1 Connect the sets of
numbered dots in
order, to finish
3 9 the dolphin.

10

1

Follow the trails to see
where each jellyfish goes.

2

5

4 3

Find and circle 3 more
pufferfish, like this one.

Animals of North America

Use the pen to show the brown bear the way to his family by the river.

Draw over the dotted lines to finish the moose's antlers.

Write an X under the eagle that does not match any other.

Circle another wolf that looks just like this one.

Australian animals

Which kangaroo will do more jumps? Trace over the trails and count the jumps to find out.

Connect the numbered dots in order, to finish the mother kangaroo.

Find and circle 3 more kookaburras, like this one.

Spot 3 differences between the two koalas below.

Circle the echidna below that does not match any other.

Creepy-crawlies

Draw lines between the dragonflies that match each other.

Follow the trails to see which butterfly lands on the flower.

Draw over the
dotted lines to
finish the web.

Find and circle
5 caterpillars.

Count the ants below, then
trace over the correct number.

7   6   8

In a bamboo forest

Spot 3 differences between these two red pandas.

Draw more marks on the snow leopard.

Draw over the
dotted lines to finish
the flying squirrels.

Connect the numbered dots
in order, to finish the panda.

In icy lands

Use the pen to show the polar bear cub the way to her mother and brother.

Draw over the dotted lines to finish the narwhal tusks.

Count the seals on each ice floe,
then trace over the numbers.

5

2

6

Find and circle 6
more Arctic hares,
like this one.

On a jungle island

Count the stripes on each lemur's tail, then trace over the numbers.

8

7

9

Draw more stripes on these lemurs' tails so each tail has 10 stripes.

Spot 5 differences between these two snakes.

Connect the numbered dots in order, to finish the chameleon.

Out at night

Draw over the dotted lines to finish the owls.

Spot 5 differences between these two foxes.

Find and circle 3 more hedgehogs, like this one.

Use the pen to finish the bats' wings.

Follow the trails to see which hole each rabbit will run to.

Usborne

Wipe-Clean

Animal Activities

This fun book is a perfect way for young children to develop their counting, observation and pen control skills.

Educational Development Corporation

Published in the USA by EDC PUBLISHING
5402 S. 122nd E. Avenue, Tulsa, Oklahoma 74146, USA.

NOT FOR SALE OUTSIDE OF THE USA

$7.99

JFMAMJJ SOND/19
05009/01

Made with paper from a sustainable source.

⚠ **WARNING:**
CHOKING HAZARD—Small parts.
Not for children under 3 yrs.

Ink from pen may not be washable.
This product conforms to ASTM D 4236.

www.edcpub.com or
www.usbornebooksandmore.com

$2.99

448086
m44
434–B

ISBN 978-0-7945-4670-0

9 780794 546700